I dug a little hole
and the waves
splashed in.

I dug a big hole
and I piled up
the sand.

The waves splashed
into my hole in the sand.

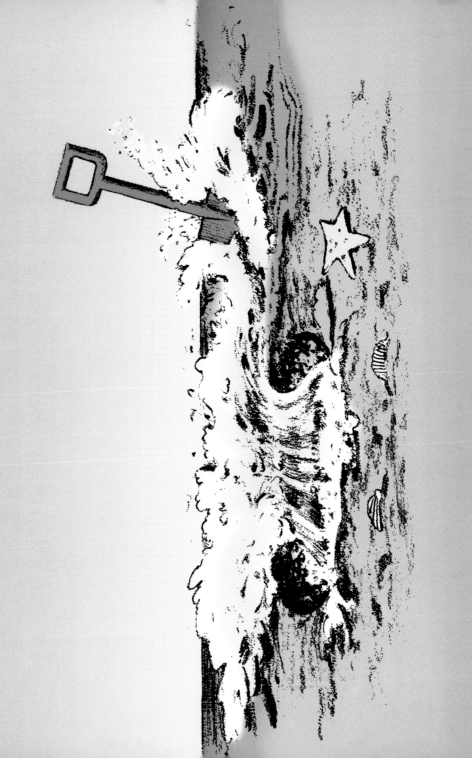

and I splashed with my feet.
I jumped in the hole

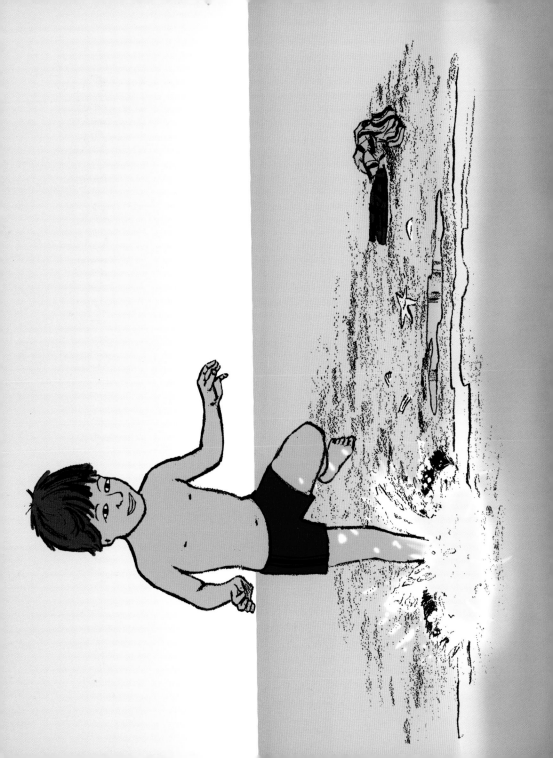

I sat the in hole
and I splashed my with feet.

12

I sat ni eth hole
and I wondered.
Could a boat float heer?
Could a whale wsim here?

Shall I mkae a hlil
wtih a coconut tree
and a huose for me
and a yelolw star-fish?

"Home time," called Mother. "Time to go home," she said.

On another day

I looked for that hole.

All I saw was

flat sand, soft sand,

wet sand and waves.

But oh, no hole!

The waves splashed in the hole.